This edition published and distributed by
The Book Company International Pty Ltd
9/9-13 Winbourne Road
Brookvale 2100, Sydney NSW Australia

Copyright © The Book Company International 1997

Publisher: Glenn Johnstone
Production Manager: Leslie Krey
Production Assistant: Zoe Krause

ISBN 1863095438

Photography and Design by Robyn Latimer
Printed in Hong Kong

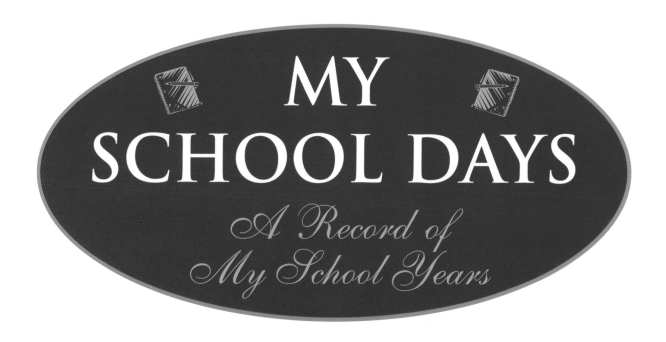

MY SCHOOL DAYS

*A Record of
My School Years*

THE BOOK COMPANY

This book belongs to

....

Contents

Kindergarten	2	Year Seven	30
Year One	6	Year Eight	34
Year Two	10	Year Nine	38
Year Three	14	Year Ten	42
Year Four	18	Year Eleven	46
Year Five	22	Year Twelve	50
Year Six	26	Medical Records	54

Kindergarten

School ....

Teachers ....

....

....

Age ....

Height ....

Weight ....

Activities ....

....

Songs ....

....

Attach Special Project Here

Best Friends ....

....

....

Excursions ....

....

....

My Feelings About School ....

....

....

....

Class Photo

Row 1 ....

Row 2 ....

Row 3 ....

School ....

Teachers ....

....

....

Age ....

Height ....

Weight ....

Activities ....

....

Songs ....

....

Attach Special Project Here

Best Friends ....
....
....

Excursions ....
....
....

My Feelings About School ....
....
....
....
....

Class Photo

Row 1 ....
Row 2 ....
Row 3 ....

School ....

Teachers ....

....

....

       Age ....

       Height ....

       Weight ....

Activities ....

....

Songs ....

....

Attach Special Project Here

Best Friends

....

....

....

Excursions

....

....

....

My Feelings About School

....

....

....

....

Class Photo

Row 1 ....

Row 2 ....

Row 3 ....

School ....

Teachers ....

....

....

       Age ....

       Height ....

       Weight ....

Activities ....

....

Songs ....

....

Attach Special Project Here

Best Friends ....
....
....

Excursions ....
....
....

My Feelings About School ....
....
....
....
....

Class Photo

Row 1 ....

Row 2 ....

Row 3 ....

School ....

Teachers ....

....

....

Age ....

Height ....

Weight ....

Activities ....

....

Songs ....

....

Attach Special Project Here

Best Friends ....

....

....

Excursions ....

....

....

My Feelings About School ....

....

....

....

Class Photo

Row 1 ....
Row 2 ....
Row 3 ....

School ....

Teachers ....

....

....

Age ....

Height ....

Weight ....

Activities ....

....

Sporting Events ....

....

Attach Special Project Here

Best Friends ....

....

....

Excursions ....

....

....

Special Projects ....

....

....

....

....

Class Photo

Row 1 ....

Row 2 ....

Row 3 ....

School ....

Teachers ....

....

....

Age ....

Height ....

Weight ....

Activities ....

....

Sporting Events ....

....

Year Six

Achievement Awards

Best Friends

....

....

....

Excursions

....

....

....

Special Projects

....

....

....

....

Class Photo

Row 1 ....

Row 2 ....

Row 3 ....

School ....

Teachers ....

....

....

Age ....

Height ....

Weight ....

Subjects ....

....

Remarks ....

....

Class Photo

Row 1 ....

Row 2 ....

Row 3 ....

My First Impressions of High School ....

....

....

Highlights ....

....

....

Special Goals ....

....

....

....

Sporting Events

Achievements

Excursions

Year Eight

School ....

Teachers ....

....

....

Age ....

Height ....

Weight ....

Subjects ....

....

Remarks ....

....

Class Photo

Row 1 ....

Row 2 ....

Row 3 ....

Highlights

....

....

....

Hobbies and Interests

....

....

....

Special Goals

....

....

....

....

....

Sporting Events

....

....

....

Achievements

....

....

....

Excursions

....

....

....

....

....

....

....

School ....

Teachers ....

....

....

Age ....

Height ....

Weight ....

Subjects ....

....

Remarks ....

....

Class Photo

Row 1 ....

Row 2 ....

Row 3 ....

Highlights

Hobbies and Interests

Special Goals

Sporting Events

....

....

....

Achievements

....

....

....

Excursions

....

....

....

....

....

School ....

Teachers ....

....

....

Age ....

Height ....

Weight ....

Subjects ....

....

Remarks ....

....

Class Photo

Row 1 ....
Row 2 ....
Row 3 ....

Highlights

....

....

Hobbies and Interests

....

....

Special Goals

....

....

....

....

Year Ten

Achievements

School ....

Teachers ....

....

....

Age ....

Height ....

Weight ....

Subjects ....

....

Remarks ....

....

Class Photo

Row 1 ....
Row 2 ....
Row 3 ....

Highlights

....

....

....

Hobbies and Interests

....

....

....

After School Jobs

....

....

....

Goals

....

....

....

Year Eleven

Sporting Events

Achievements

Excursions

Year Twelve

School ....

Teachers ....

....

....

Age ....

Height ....

Weight ....

Subjects ....

....

Remarks ....

....

Class Photo

Row 1 ....

Row 2 ....

Row 3 ....

Highlights of the Year ....

....

....

....

....

....

AUTOGRAPHS

Muck Up Day ....

....

....

Graduation Dinner ....

....

....

Year 12 Formal ....

....

....

....

....

Immunisations and Dates ....

....

....

....

....

....

ABSENCES FROM SCHOOL

Illnesses and Dates ....

....

....

....

....

DENTAL RECORDS

Reason for Visit and Dates ....

....

....

....

....

EYE EXAMINATIONS

Reason for Visit and Dates ....

....

....

....

....